African Wildlife

QUIZ BOOK

Clive Gibson & Patrick Flood

STRUIK
NATURE

Published by Struik Nature
(an imprint of Random House Struik (Pty) Ltd)
Reg. No. 1966/003153/07
Wembley Square, First Floor, Solan Road, Gardens, Cape Town, 8001

Visit www.randomstruik.co.za and join the Struik Nature Club
for updates, news, events, and special offers.

First published in 2006
Second edition 2012

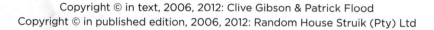

3 5 7 9 10 8 6 4 2

Copyright © in text, 2006, 2012: Clive Gibson & Patrick Flood
Copyright © in published edition, 2006, 2012: Random House Struik (Pty) Ltd

Publishing manager: Pippa Parker
Managing editor: Helen de Villiers
Design director: Janice Evans
Designer: Sean Robertson

Printed and bound by Creda Communications

ISBN 978 1 92057 280 8

Picture Credits
iStockphoto
Nigel Dennis/Images of Africa
Peter & Beverly Pickford/Images of Africa
Andrew Bannister/Images of Africa

Quiz 1

Ask each player the same question and record their answers on a separate sheet of paper. Record their scores (✔ or ✗) in the spaces provided.
The correct answers are on page 52.

QUESTIONS	PLAYERS				
	1	2	3	4	5
1. What is a klipspringer?					
2. Which game park in the Eastern Cape is famous for its elephants?					
3. Which is the only potentially deadly spider found in South Africa?					
4. To which group do frogs belong?					
5. Which African mammal is responsible for the most human deaths?					
6. During which season do leaves fall from the trees?					
7. Complete the saying: She has a memory like...					
8. What is another name for a hyrax?					
9. What part of a flower produces the pollen?					
10. Which mosquito bites humans – male or female?					
11. What African fox has large cupped ears?					
12. What is a crake?					
13. Which game park is named after a past president?					
14. A swarm of which insects can – in 24 hours – consume the amount of food necessary to feed 2 million people?					
15. What may a rinkhals do when threatened?					
16. Which African antelope can run the fastest?					
17. What sound does a hyaena make?					
18. What is a female fox known as?					
19. What is a group of baboons called?					
20. What kind of insect is an 'old lady'?					
Total					

DID YOU KNOW?
It takes a baby elephant six months to learn how to control its trunk.

Wordsearch

Find the 'creepy-crawlies'

The names of 25 different arachnids and insects are hidden horizontally and vertically in the grid below. Draw a circle around each one and record it on the list. The first one has been found for you. Why not make a photocopy of the grid for each of the players? Ask someone to time you and see who can find all the answers first. The answer grid is on page 52.

A	P	H	I	D	G	T	B	G	T	B	G	C	E	N	T	I	P	E	D	E	C	V	C	C
C	V	R	T	Y	G	T	B	G	T	B	G	I	Z	U	E	P	Z	U	O	P	R	E	R	O
R	E	S	T	I	N	K	B	U	G	G	T	C	U	H	R	R	X	E	S	T	M	A	N	C
S	T	V	A	S	Z	U	O	P	Z	G	T	A	O	S	M	V	A	R	F	O	S	R	V	K
E	E	T	G	E	B	E	E	T	L	E	V	D	O	E	I	Z	G	L	T	O	E	T	Z	R
F	O	I	T	V	A	R	G	T	B	G	T	A	M	T	T	W	X	Y	A	M	T	H	W	O
L	O	C	E	Z	G	L	G	T	B	G	T	V	O	S	E	V	A	R	M	O	S	W	V	A
E	M	K	D	W	X	Y	M	O	S	Q	U	I	T	O	U	O	P	U	P	O	E	O	Z	C
A	O	S	G	V	A	R	U	O	P	Z	U	O	P	Z	P	Z	X	P	A	M	T	R	W	H
U	O	P	R	U	O	T	P	Z	I	P	O	R	E	D	R	O	M	A	N	O	S	M	V	S
D	Z	X	A	P	Z	G	G	T	D	O	S	T	V	A	R	O	S	T	R	O	E	E	Z	M
R	T	E	S	G	T	W	C	V	E	O	E	E	Z	G	L	O	E	C	R	S	C	K	E	I
A	V	B	S	C	V	E	R	E	R	M	F	I	S	H	M	O	T	H	O	C	U	O	P	L
G	E	D	H	R	E	E	A	G	X	O	S	T	V	A	R	O	S	P	Z	O	P	Z	X	L
O	S	T	O	A	G	V	Z	D	A	M	S	E	L	F	L	Y	K	G	T	R	G	T	E	I
N	E	E	P	Z	E	I	U	O	P	I	U	O	P	G	T	B	G	C	V	P	C	V	B	P
F	T	D	P	U	O	L	P	Z	X	T	P	F	I	R	E	F	L	Y	E	I	R	E	D	E
L	S	T	E	P	Z	A	G	T	E	E	G	T	E	U	O	P	U	A	G	O	A	G	F	D
Y	E	E	R	G	T	B	C	V	B	F	C	R	I	C	K	E	T	Z	E	N	Z	E	U	E

- ☑ Aphid
- ☐ Beetle
- ☐ Centipede
- ☐ Cicada
- ☐ Cockroach
- ☐ Cricket
- ☐ Damselfly
- ☐ Dragonfly
- ☐ Earthworm
- ☐ Firefly
- ☐ Fishmoth
- ☐ Flea
- ☐ Grasshopper
- ☐ Millipede
- ☐ Mite
- ☐ Mosquito
- ☐ Red Roman
- ☐ Scorpion
- ☐ Spider
- ☐ Stinkbug
- ☐ Tampan
- ☐ Termite
- ☐ Tick
- ☐ Weevil

DID YOU KNOW?
The sound of a single cricket seems to come from several directions.

True or false? 1

Some of the following statements are true and some are false. Record each person's answers (T or F) in the spaces provided and check the correct answers on page 52.

STATEMENTS	PLAYERS				
	1	2	3	4	5
1. A sable antelope is so dangerous that lions are wary of attacking it.					
2. The blesbok is darker in colour than the bontebok.					
3. A female gemsbok has longer horns than the male.					
4. The aardwolf is a type of hyaena.					
5. A porcupine can shoot its quills (spines).					
6. A springhare has no claws on its front feet.					
7. Female mountain reedbuck don't have horns.					
8. An impala can jump over a fence 3 m high.					
9. Grey rhebok are known to kill sheep and goats.					
10. Bats have large eyes.					
11. Anti-venom is made from snake venom.					
12. Snakes can swim.					
13. Dodos could not fly.					
14. A chameleon turns its head rather than its body to look behind it.					
15. A squid can change its colour.					
Total					

DID YOU KNOW?

A group of foraging meerkats will have a member of the group on lookout constantly to scan the sky and land for signs of danger.

5

What's that word? 1

Ask each player to identify the meaning of the following words and record their answers in the spaces provided. Check the correct answers on page 52

WORD	A	B	C	PLAYERS 1	2	3	4	5
1. Striated	Spotted or ribbed	Grooved or striped	Smooth, lacking markings					
2. Forb	Herb for the treatment of rabies	A broad-leaved herbaceous plant	An evergreen shrub					
3. Raptor	Flying dinosaur	Bird of prey	Flying squirrel					
4. Lactating	Breeding	Secreting milk	Birds regurgitating food for their young					
5. Brisket	The chest of an animal	A type of rough bark on a tree	A wild fruit					
6. Arboreal	Seen only at night	Living in trees	Coming from Africa					
7. Perennial	Underground water	Through all the seasons of the year	Once a year					
8. Leveret	A bird's nest in a tree	A fork in a tree	A young hare					
9. Scat	An animal's faecal dropping	Marks left by leopards on trees to indicate their territories	Leaves eaten by kudu					
10. Vivarium	A small indoor garden	An enclosure prepared for keeping animals in conditions similar to their natural habitat	A garden grown in a bottle					
11. Cytotoxin	Poison attacking cells and tissues	Antivenom for poison attacking cells and tissues	Poison affecting the nervous system					
12. Biannual	A type of aloe	Twice yearly	A leaf that has two separate parts					
Total								

DID YOU KNOW?
Giraffes have very high blood pressure in order for their blood to travel to the head.

Crossword 1

Answers on p 52.

HINT!

Across 25: Southern African plant used extensively in skin creams

Across

3 The sea animals with the strongest jaws (6)

5 This bird lays its eggs in the nests of other birds (6)

7 The largest animal without a backbone (5)

8 A baby oyster (4)

9 This constellation of stars can be used to find south (8,5)

12 A bird grabs food with this (4)

13 A very leggy creature (9)

15 Pigs with tusks (7)

19 They are said to be wise (4)

21 Swimming mammal (7)

23 Protective layer around the earth (5)

24 Snake-like fish (3)

25 Southern African plant used extensively in skin creams (4)

26 The only flying mammal in the world (3)

Down

1 Reptiles rely on the sun for... (4,4)

2 A group of whales (3)

4 The group of animals to which turtles belong (8)

6 A zebra that has shadow stripes between the darker stripes (9)

10 This bird lays the biggest eggs (7)

11 A poisonous mushroom (5,3)

12 Bird's wings _____ up and down (4)

14 The sea animal that makes the loudest noise (5)

16 A zebra's feet (6)

17 Small sea animals that filter water for food (7)

18 Fine-leafed vegetation that dominates the Cape region of South Africa (6)

20 A blind, burrowing mammal (4)

21 A lion's home (3)

22 A shell that clings! (6)

Multiple choice quiz 1

Allocate each player a number and record his or her choice under the relevant number. Check for the correct answers on page 52.

QUESTIONS	PLAYERS				
	1	2	3	4	5
1. What is a hinged terrapin? a) A reptile b) An insect c) A mammal					
2. What is a gladiolus? a) A flower b) An insect c) A spider					
3. What does indigenous mean? a) Foreign to an area b) Occurring naturally in an area c) Extinct in an area					
4. What is an agapanthus? a) A flower b) A cat c) An insect					
5. Which mushroom is edible? a) Fly agaric b) Field mushroom c) Panther cap					
6. What is a group of hyaenas called? a) A clan b) A herd c) A troop					
7. What is a serval? a) A cat b) A fish c) A bat					
8. What colour are common arum lilies? a) Red b) White c) Blue					
9. What is oology? a) The study of birds' eggs b) The study of reproductive cycles c) The study of animal populations					
10. A sponge is... a) an animal b) a plant c) bacteria					

DID YOU KNOW?

When crocodile eggs are ready to hatch, the 'babies' make a squeaking sound that alerts the mother; she then removes the soil covering the eggs and the babies break out.

QUESTIONS continued

	1	2	3	4	5
11. How do crocodiles lose heat?					
a) Through their skin					
b) Through their mouths					
c) Through their feet					
12. How do frogs breathe under water?					
a) Through their skin					
b) Through their lungs					
c) Neither A nor B					
13. Which are the only mammals that can fly?					
a) Hawks					
b) Ostriches					
c) Bats					
14. On which jaw do elephant's tusks grow?					
a) Upper					
b) Lower					
c) Neither					
15. What is the fin on a fish's back called?					
a) Dorsal fin					
b) Scalar fin					
c) Ventral fin					
16. Which bee has a sting?					
a) A queen bee					
b) A worker bee					
c) A guard bee					
17. Which is the biggest antelope?					
a) Eland					
b) Kudu					
c) Buffalo					
18. What does diurnal mean?					
a) Active during daylight					
b) To repeat an action twice					
c) Seen only at night					
19. How does an otter retrieve the meat from inside a crab's hard shell?					
a) It bites into the hard shell with its strong jaws					
b) It tears the shell open with its sharp claws					
c) It hits the crab against a rock until the shell cracks open					
20. What is a rhino's horn made of?					
a) Ivory					
b) Bone					
c) Compressed hair					
Total					

DID YOU KNOW?

Parts of the Shepherd's tree are used to treat epilepsy.

Quiz 2

Ask each player the same question and record their answers on a separate sheet of paper. Record their scores (✔ or ✘) in the spaces provided.
The correct answers are on page 52.

QUESTIONS	PLAYERS				
	1	2	3	4	5
1. Which is the smallest antelope in South Africa?					
2. What colour is the face of a Ross's Loerie?					
3. What is a darter?					
4. How do kingfishers kill their prey?					
5. What is a distinguishing feature of a waterbuck?					
6. What gave the hamerkop its name?					
7. The sable antelope's coat has two colours. What are they?					
8. In times of drought a mother elephant will do what to cool her calf?					
9. What is the dominant colour of a female ostrich?					
10. Do dragonflies have stings?					
11. What does the term 'crepuscular' mean?					
12. What is a baby elephant called?					
13. In conservation, what do the letters WWF stand for?					
14. In what country are black wattles indigenous?					
15. Which are the largest ferns in South Africa?					
16. What is another name for a caracal?					
17. In which direction do the sable's horns point?					
18. Which sex of the red duiker has horns?					
19. What has the urine of rock rabbits (dassies) been used for in southern Africa?					
20. What is the collective noun for a group of fish swimming in the same direction?					
Total					

DID YOU KNOW?
A bushbaby can leap about 33 times the length of its own body. That is a full 5 m.

What's that word? 2

Ask each player to identify the meaning of the following words and record their answers in the spaces provided. Check the correct answers on page 52.

WORD	A	B	C	PLAYERS 1	2	3	4	5
1. Pelagic	Found in rivers	Of the open sea	Found in large inland lakes					
2. Nocturnal	Living in shrubs and low bushes	Active at night	Feeding on flying insects					
3. Pronking	The bobbing movement of a heron stalking its prey	The low, rumbling sound made by elephants	Bouncing vertically on all four legs as do springbok					
4. Browsing	Feeding on leaves, twigs and shoots of trees and shrubs	The dancing performed by a pair of secretarybirds during mating	The mating technique of tilapia fish					
5. Nagana	A small monkey seen mostly at night	A flesh-eating reptile from the Limpopo valley	Sleeping sickness					
6. Rufous	Rough	The shape of volcanic rock	Reddish-brown in colour					
7. Montane	Inhabiting mountainous regions	A hard wax obtained from trees	The sporadic occurrence of large boulders					
8. Feral	Tame	Wild	Long					
9. Termitaria	The droppings of a colony of ants	The nests of termites	The trail of destruction left by ants					
10. Copse	A thicket of trees or shrubs	The crest of a hill	A rocky outcrop on a plateau					
11. Pristine	Erect	Unspoilt	Well-watered					
12. Natant	Swimming or floating on water	Submerged in water	The swelling caused by a bee-sting					
Total								

DID YOU KNOW?
A rat can last longer without water than can a camel.

11

Multiple choice quiz 2

Allocate each player a number and record his or her choice under the relevant number. Check for the correct answers on page 53.

QUESTIONS	PLAYERS				
	1	2	3	4	5
1. Which tree's pungent flowers attract pollinators? a) Stinkwood tree b) Shepherd's tree c) Silver tree					
2. Which part of the body does a mamba's venom affect? a) Nervous system b) Heart c) Eyes					
3. What do fungi produce in order to reproduce? a) Spores b) Seeds c) Tubules					
4. In which direction do the rear flippers of a seal point? a) Forwards b) Backwards c) Sideways					
5. The woody tube system that transports water in plants is ... a) the vascular system b) the pipe system c) the cardio system					
6. The venom of which fish can be fatal to humans? a) Butterfish b) Stonefish c) Neither					
7. What colour are the flowers of baobab trees? a) Scarlet red b) Royal blue c) Snow white					
8. What type of plant is a horsetail? a) A flower b) A weed c) A fern					
9. What type of animal is a black-necked agama? a) A bird b) A frog c) A lizard					
10. What useful substance does the bark of conifers contain? a) Water b) Hydrogen c) Tannin					

DID YOU KNOW?
A newborn giraffe is about 2 m tall!

QUESTIONS continued

	1	2	3	4	5
11. Which type of snake was once recorded to have eaten a tortoise? a) Berg adder b) Puffadder c) Snouted night adder					
12. Which seahorse becomes 'pregnant' and incubates the eggs? a) The male b) The female c) Both the male and female					
13. What is photosynthesis? a) Two animals that look almost identical b) Plants using the sun's energy to produce food c) When flowers move to show their face to the sun					
14. What are corals? a) Animals b) Plants c) Shells					
15. Where are a locust's ears situated? a) On the side of the head b) Behind the last pair of legs c) On the front of the head					
16. Which is the largest rodent in South Africa? a) A rat b) A porcupine c) A squirrel					
17. What is the dominant baboon male called? a) Alpha male b) Pilot male c) Leader male					
18. Which sex of wildebeest has horns? a) Males b) Females c) Both sexes					
19. What colour is the underside of a kudu's tail? a) White b) Brown c) Tan					
20. Which is the biggest African snake? a) The cobra b) The puffadder c) The African rock python					
Total					

DID YOU KNOW?
Dolphins sleep with one eye open!

Crossword 2

Answers on p 53.

HINT!
Down 13: The larva of a moth or butterfly

Across

2 To pass the winter months in a dormant or inactive state (9)

5 Pointed mouthparts used to inject venom (5)

6 A dangerous animal that allows small birds to clean its teeth but doesn't harm them (9)

8 The rear section of an insect's body (7)

11 Bird with a wagging tail (7)

13 The means used to blend with the surroundings. (10)

16 Simple living things that are not plants or animals (5)

17 A spider that shares its name with a primate (6)

20 Animals that eat members of their own species (9)

21 The preserved remains of a long dead animal (6)

23 The process by which a young insect changes into its adult form (13)

Down

1 Simple plant-like living things (5)

3 Tiger of the sea (9)

4 A six-sided space in the nest of a bee or wasp (4)

7 The coming together of both sexes of animals to produce young (6)

9 A male bee that mates with the queen (5)

10 Movement of animals in search of food (9)

12 Land and water based animal (9)

13 The larva of a moth or butterfly (11)

14 A term that describes many insect larvae (4)

15 The silken case that protects insects' pupae (6)

18 Shedding of old skin or hair (8)

19 An animal on which a parasite lives and feeds (4)

22 Fish eggs (3)

Quiz 3

Ask each player the same question and record their answers on a separate sheet of paper. Record their scores (✔ or ✘) in the spaces provided.
The correct answers are on page 53.

QUESTIONS	PLAYERS				
	1	2	3	4	5
1. What colour is the chest of the Purple-crested Loerie?					
2. What is the Afrikaans name for a bushbaby?					
3. What is parthenogenesis?					
4. What do you call a snakebite where no venom is injected?					
5. What creature can change its colour?					
6. Which bird stores food in a pouch below its beak?					
7. What is a ground hornbill's favourite food?					
8. Do lizards have eyelids?					
9. Why don't birds eat ladybirds?					
10. Where do wasps enter their nests?					
11. Why do snakes shed their skin?					
12. What is the name given to the egg case of some sharks?					
13. To which group do snails belong?					
14. What is a baby zebra called?					
15. Which insects kill more people than all other creatures combined?					
16. Which internal organs do insects lack?					
17. What does the term 'apterous' mean?					
18. What is a chincherinchee?					
19. Which unusual tree is protected by law in South Africa?					
20. What is the tongue of a mollusc called?					
Total					

DID YOU KNOW?

The black rhinoceros weighs up to 1 020 kg, and charges at a speed of about 45 km per hour.

Multiple choice quiz 3

Allocate each player a number and record his or her choice under the relevant number. Check for the correct answers on page 53.

QUESTIONS	PLAYERS				
	1	2	3	4	5
1. Which holds more oxygen? a) Hot water b) Warm water c) Cold water					
2. What do adult birds lack? a) Teeth b) Lungs c) Skin					
3. Which of the following apply to fish? a) Warm-blooded b) Cold-blooded c) They have pink blood					
4. Which of the following is an example of a mollusc? a) White mussel b) Shark c) Whale					
5. What do molluscs lack? a) Eyes b) Vertebrae c) Tentacles					
6. Vampire bats will... a) adopt orphans b) risk their lives to share food with less fortunate bats c) Both A & B					
7. In terms of diet, what describes starfish? a) Herbivorous b) Carnivorous c) Omnivorous					
8. A scute is... a) a type of bacteria b) the feathers that form the crest of a guinea fowl c) the horny plate on the shell of a tortoise					
9. Dung beetles get their name from the fact that they... a) breed in dung b) are often mistaken for mammal droppings c) play in dung					
10. What is a group of dassies (rock rabbits) called? a) A troop b) A pack c) A colony					

DID YOU KNOW?

No two zebras have the same stripe patterns.

QUESTIONS continued

	1	2	3	4	5

11. Which member of the cat family has the longest ears?
a) A lion
b) A leopard
c) A caracal

12. Which way do the stripes run on a zebra's legs?
a) Across their legs
b) Down their legs
c) Neither. There are no leg stripes.

13. Echolocation is the means by which porpoises and dolphins ...
a) navigate.
b) locate their prey.
c) communicate.

14. Which substance enables a plant to make food for itself?
a) Chlorine
b) Hydrochloric acid
c) Chlorophyll

15. What do conifers produce?
a) Flowers
b) Cones
c) Flowers and cones

16. How many legs does a spider have?
a) 4
b) 6
c) 8

17. Which type of water freezes at the lowest temperature?
a) Salt water
b) Fresh water
c) River water

18. How do plants absorb minerals?
a) Through their roots
b) From the air
c) Through their leaves

19. What is another name for a sand prawn?
a) Pink prawn
b) Tiger prawn
c) Langoustine

20. A worm lizard is a type of...
a) worm
b) gecko
c) snake

Total

DID YOU KNOW?
Adult eland bulls can easily jump over a 2-m-high game fence and have been known to jump over each other for seemingly no reason.

Which animal am I?

Read the following descriptions of African animals one at a time and ask each player to identify what has been described. Allow them 20 seconds to answer. Check for the correct answers on page 53 and record the players' scores in the space provided. If they don't answer in time they miss the round.

CLUES	PLAYERS 1	2	3	4	5
1. I usually move in a small, temporary herd browsing on leaves and young twigs. I defend myself by kicking with my front and back legs. I have to spread my legs to drink water, but can go without water for a long time.					
2. I have a pointed upper lip and a horn. I can have a very bad temper and can be aggressive. I have ivory teeth.					
3. I move in herds of up to 30. I have a long tail that is dark at the base and almost pure white at the end.					
4. I can't see or hear very well but I have an excellent sense of smell. I usually move in large herds in forests or plains close to water.					
5. I always hunt at night, and often take my kills up a tree. I can be dangerous if you confront me.					
6. I come out at night to burrow for termites and ants. I can live for up to 12 years. I have a sticky tongue.					
7. I live mostly on boulders and rocky hills. Despite being a vegetarian, I can inflict quite a serious bite. I live in colonies of around 60 animals. You will know that I am in the area as the surrounding rocks and boulders will be stained with black and white streaks from my urine.					
8. I have enormous ears that I put close to the ground to hear insects underground. I feed on insects, termites, snakes, small birds, mice and wild fruit. I can double back on my tracks when running at high speed and am called the "Draaijakkals" in Afrikaans because of this.					
Total					

DID YOU KNOW?

A few strips of the bark of the terminalia tree can be used to make a strong rope.

Wordsearch

Find the birds

The names of 25 different birds are hidden horizontally and vertically in the grid below. Draw a circle around each one and record it on the list. The first one has been found for you. Why not make a photocopy of the grid for each of the players? Ask someone to time you and see who can find all the answers first. The answer grid is on page 53.

S	E	C	R	E	T	A	R	Y	B	I	R	D	Z	S	D	R	Y	U	O	P	G	U	L	L
A	S	D	F	G	H	J	K	L	Q	W	E	R	T	Y	U	I	O	P	Z	X	C	V	B	N
B	N	P	E	N	G	U	I	N	H	J	K	L	Q	D	Y	D	F	G	T	E	F	S	F	D
S	H	E	Z	X	C	V	B	N	S	D	R	Y	U	A	O	Z	X	C	V	B	N	H	Y	A
E	R	T	M	N	B	V	C	X	A	L	B	A	T	R	O	S	S	R	E	D	T	E	O	B
T	Y	R	S	R	Y	E	O	S	T	V	A	R	Q	T	S	A	S	A	G	F	Y	R	M	C
G	N	E	E	L	Y	G	O	E	E	Z	G	L	I	E	E	V	X	Z	E	U	U	O	C	H
D	M	L	T	Y	R	R	M	T	D	W	X	Y	P	R	T	P	E	L	I	C	A	N	J	I
A	A	D	D	G	G	E	Z	X	E	M	O	E	U	Y	R	B	N	Y	M	Z	A	W	B	C
T	E	R	N	P	Q	T	V	N	Y	J	S	D	E	P	L	O	V	E	R	J	K	X	V	K
A	S	D	F	H	H	G	J	K	L	O	T	P	I	U	Y	T	R	Q	E	W	I	M	B	G
Q	U	A	I	L	O	K	L	S	T	O	R	K	X	S	W	S	P	O	O	N	B	I	L	L
H	Q	R	W	T	R	I	P	Y	J	M	I	T	I	P	S	S	P	W	B	T	I	R	N	K
A	A	G	O	O	S	E	K	E	R	Q	C	G	J	K	E	T	I	T	S	S	S	F	B	M
D	Z	V	X	B	D	H	N	B	F	A	H	B	M	M	R	C	D	Z	R	W	G	B	V	W
U	Q	Q	F	L	A	M	I	N	G	O	Z	X	C	V	G	U	I	N	E	A	F	O	W	L
C	S	D	F	H	B	E	U	Y	R	B	N	Y	M	T	E	U	Y	R	B	N	Y	M	W	U
K	K	J	U	I	C	D	E	R	H	A	V	O	C	E	T	E	R	H	J	D	D	Y	A	S
O	F	R	A	N	C	O	L	I	N	T	R	Q	E	O	P	I	H	A	M	E	R	K	O	P

- ☑ Albatross
- ☐ Avocet
- ☐ Dabchick
- ☐ Darter
- ☐ Duck
- ☐ Egret
- ☐ Flamingo
- ☐ Francolin
- ☐ Goose
- ☐ Guineafowl
- ☐ Gull
- ☐ Hamerkop
- ☐ Heron
- ☐ Ibis
- ☐ Ostrich
- ☐ Pelican
- ☐ Penguin
- ☐ Petrel
- ☐ Plover
- ☐ Quail
- ☐ Secretarybird
- ☐ Spoonbill
- ☐ Stork
- ☐ Tern
- ☐ Tit

DID YOU KNOW?
Warthogs can run at up to 50 km per hour.

19

Multiple choice quiz 4

Allocate each player a number and record his or her choice under the relevant number. Check for the correct answers on page 53.

QUESTIONS	PLAYERS				
	1	2	3	4	5
1. What are elephants' tusks made of? a) Ivory b) Ivorian fibre c) Compressed hair					
2. Which animal lives in a holt? a) An otter b) An aardvark c) A mongoose					
3. Which is the heaviest meat-eater? a) A cheetah b) A lion c) A leopard					
4. For how long is an elephant pregnant? a) 9 months b) 22 months c) 24 months					
5. What is a honey badger's home called? a) A den b) A sett c) A burrow					
6. What does an otter use to steer itself? a) Its tail b) Its back legs c) Its ears					
7. The only seal indigenous to southern African coastline is... a) the Cape fur seal b) the Southern elephant seal c) the Sub-Antarctic fur seal					
8. What do whales use to keep warm? a) Their blood b) Each other c) Their blubber (fat)					
9. What do bats use to find their way around? a) Touch b) Sight c) Sonar					
10. Fruit bats are also known as... a) flying foxes b) orchard bats c) sweet bats					

DID YOU KNOW?

In one day, a large bull elephant can eat the equivalent of 612 Lunch Bars and drink the equivalent of 320 cans of Coke!

QUESTIONS continued

11. Which lions hunt more often, males or females?
a) Males
b) Females
c) Both

12. Which jaw can a shark move?
a) Lower jaw
b) Upper jaw
c) Both jaws

13. On which fin is the spot of the blackspot shark?
a) Not on a fin
b) 2nd dorsal fin
c) 1st dorsal fin

14. Which is the largest member of the dolphin family?
a) Killer whale
b) Common dolphin
c) Bottlenose dolphin

15. Complete the sentence: A chameleon's tongue is ... the length of its body.
a) exactly
b) twice
c) three times

16. What does the word hippopotamus mean?
a) River horse
b) Pot belly
c) River cow

17. How do the king and ordinary cheetah differ?
a) The king cheetah is bigger
b) The king cheetah has stripes
c) The ordinary cheetah has stripes

18. Why do cheetahs kill prey by suffocation?
a) Their canine teeth are too short
b) Their canine teeth are too weak
c) Their molar teeth are too short

19. Why don't hippos get sunburnt?
a) Their sweat acts as a sunscreen
b) Their dark skin colour protects them
c) They lie under water for protection from the sun

20. An elephant does not use trumpeting for...
a) indicating excitement
b) greeting
c) to signal that it has found food

Total

DID YOU KNOW?
The pattern of spots at the root of a lion's whiskers is unique to each animal.

Crossword 3

Answers on p 54.

Across

3 The nutrient-rich liquid found in plants (3)

4 Birds of peace (5)

7 Upper ridge of a bird's bill (6)

8 Fold of loose skin hanging from the throat (6)

10 Type of bird of prey (5)

12 Main central vein of a leaf (6)

17 The insects in a social colony that build the nest and find the food (7)

18 These grow on riverbanks (5)

20 A network of silken threads woven by a spider (3)

21 Plant with fleshy, juicy tissue containing water reserves (9)

22 A single-celled microscopic animal (6)

23 Plant parts that fleshy rather than woody (10)

25 Sacred bird (4)

26 The part of a bee that it uses to hurt you if you annoy it (5)

Down

1 Grains made by the male parts of flowers (6)

2 One of the modified leaves comprising the calyx at a flower's base (5)

3 Poachers use it (also the name of a drum) (5)

5 The egg-laying female in a colony of ants (5)

6 The sugary liquid produced by plants that attracts insects (6)

9 A place where bee hives are kept (6)

11 Fossilised plant resin (5)

13 Massive protuberance at the base of horns (4)

14 Bulky in body (9)

15 Poisonous liquid used by an animal to kill or paralyse its prey (5)

16 Points on a stem from which leaves and braches grow (4)

19 Very small bird (3)

20 Where rabbits live (6)

24 Threads of protein made by spiders (4)

Which bird am I?

Read the following descriptions of African birds one at a time and ask each player to identify what has been described. Allow them 20 seconds to answer. Check for the correct answers on page 54 and record the players' scores in the space provided. If they don't answer in time they miss the round.

CLUES	PLAYERS				
	1	2	3	4	5
1. I am named for the 'quills' protruding from the back of my head. I eat snakes, birds, and tiny mammals.					
2. I migrate mainly in the summer and I make a goose-like call when flying, but you've probably seen me in shallow lagoons or lakes. I have very long legs and pinkish plumage.					
3. I am a large, graceful bird and the national bird of South Africa. I am mostly found on grasslands and in the Karoo, often in pairs or family groups.					
4. I am the most common owl in South Africa. I only come out at night when I feed on reptiles, insects and small mammals.					
5. I am the largest African eagle. I have excellent eyesight and I feed on small mammals.					
6. I am found in gardens but favour open country. I impale my prey on thorns.					
7. I have a booming call and spend most of my time on the ground. When alarmed, I fly only a short distance.					
8. I catch fish as it comes to the surface of the water, using my rear talons.					
Total					

DID YOU KNOW?
The cuckoo lays its eggs in other birds' nests and the 'adopted' parents raise the chick.

Multiple choice quiz 5

Allocate each player a number and record his or her choice under the relevant number. Check for the correct answers on page 54.

QUESTIONS	PLAYERS				
	1	2	3	4	5
1. In the common duiker, which sex is larger? a) Both are the same size b) Male c) Female					
2. Which sex of elephant has a sharper, angled head? a) Neither b) Male c) Female					
3. Which waterfall does the Otter Trail pass? a) Victoria Falls b) Storms River Falls c) Zambezi Falls					
4. Where is the Golden Gate Highlands National Park? a) In Kwazulu-Natal b) In the Free State c) In Northern Province					
5. What is an African jacana? a) A bird b) A buck c) A cat					
6. Where is the sting of a scorpion located? a) In its mouth b) At the end of its pincers c) At the end of its tail					
7. Which bird eats insects off the backs of impala and giraffes? a) Weaver b) Oxpecker c) Tick bird					
8. What does an entomologist study? a) Plants b) Animals c) Insects					
9. What is a sandpiper? a) A rodent b) A bird c) A buck					
10. What do vultures feed on? a) Mice b) Rabbits c) Carcasses					

DID YOU KNOW?
An ostrich egg contains the equivalent of 24 free-range chicken's eggs!

QUESTIONS continued

11. What colour is the underside of a reedbuck's tail?
a) Brown
b) White
c) Red

12. Which sex of bushbuck is darker in colour?
a) Male
b) Female
c) They are the same

13. What is white stinkwood often used for?
a) Chipboard
b) Firewood
c) Furniture

14. What is a group of dogs called?
a) A pack
b) A clan
c) A kennel

15. From where does an oyster mushroom get its name?
a) Its appearance
b) Its feel
c) Its taste

16. What is a colobus?
a) A monkey
b) A rat
c) A bird

17. Browsers are animals that eat...
a) meat.
b) grass.
c) leaves.

18. A tortoise pulls its head and limbs back into its shell...
a) in order to shelter from rain
b) because it is painfully shy
c) to protect its vulnerable parts from predators

19. Latex comes from the milky juice of a...
a) latex tree
b) rubber tree
c) pine tree

20. How long can an adult hippo stay under water?
a) 5 minutes
b) 10 minutes
c) 15 minutes

Total

DID YOU KNOW?
Male baboons can stand up to 1,8 m tall and weigh as much as 43 kg.

Wordsearch

Find the mammals

The names of 25 different mammals are hidden horizontally and vertically in the grid below. Draw a circle around each one and record it on the list. The first one has been found for you. Why not make a photocopy of the grid for each of the players? Ask someone to time you and see who can find all the answers first. The answer grid is on page 54.

```
B A T E R H B H Y A E N A E N C A R A C A L R H J
E R H J D Z J I U Y T Q A E R H J Y R B N R H P O
I U Y T R P T Y R B N A R I U Y T B U S H B A B Y
Y R I N Y O R E R H J D D Y R B N U E R H J R B B
R H M D D R B I U Y T R V R H J D F I U Y T E J J
E R P J B C B Y R B N Y A I U Y T F Y R B N B T T
I U A T J U J R H J D D R Y R B N A R H J D J R R
Y R L N T P H W E M O N K E Y G H L O E L A N D B
R H A D R I E U Y R B N Y M E R H O U Y T U Y T J
M U Y T B N D E R H G D D Y E R H J R B N R B N S
O R B N J E P I U Y E R Q F I U Y T R A T E R H Q
U E R H J D E R H E N H J O Y R B N E E R H J B U
S H J B A B O O N I E Y T X R E L E P H A N T J I
E E L H J E R H J Y T B N E R H J D E Y R B N H R
B I I Y T E R H J R H J D R A B B I T R H J D Y R
J Y O B N B U S H P I G E U Y R B N Y M E R H J E
H R N J D V U Y T U Y T D E R H J S E R V A L T L
E E L I W N R B N R L E O P A R D R Q E Y R B N B
S P R I N G B O K Y M C U Y T E R H C H E E T A H
```

- ☑ Aardvark
- ☐ Baboon
- ☐ Bat
- ☐ Buffalo
- ☐ Bushbaby
- ☐ Bushpig
- ☐ Caracal
- ☐ Cheetah
- ☐ Eland
- ☐ Elephant
- ☐ Fox
- ☐ Genet
- ☐ Hare
- ☐ Hyaena
- ☐ Impala
- ☐ Leopard
- ☐ Lion
- ☐ Monkey
- ☐ Mouse
- ☐ Porcupine
- ☐ Rabbit
- ☐ Rat
- ☐ Serval
- ☐ Springbok
- ☐ Squirrel

DID YOU KNOW?

You can hear porcupines approaching because their quills rattle as they walk.

What's that word? 3

Ask each player to identify the meaning of the following words and record their answers in the spaces provided. Check the correct answers on page 52.

WORD	A	B	C	PLAYERS 1	2	3	4	5
1. Aggregation	An average	A large collection	A small sample					
2. Carapace	A hard, bony outer covering, covering the head and thorax of a crustacean	A body part of an insect that resembles a car	An insect without an exoskeleton, such as a slug.					
3. Galls	Small, knob-like swellings found on the nodes of healthy plants	Small stones found in the gall bladder of any mammal	Swelling of plant tissue caused by insects, disease or injury					
4. Lupine	A type of bean	Savage, resembling a wolf	A loping type of walk					
5. Mandible	One of the bones in the foot	A member of the seal family	A mouthpart					
6. Ferret	To search	An animal used for hunting rabbits	Both of these					
7. Corolla	The central part of an elephant's ear	The bend in a river	Collective term for all the petals of a flower					
8. Hermaphrodite	A rare type of mineral	An animal born with both male and female reproductive organs	An animal that consists of only one cell					
9. Deciduous	A plant that sheds all its leaves in winter	The collective name for bananas	A disease commonly found in buffalo					
10. Spinneret	Opening on a spider's body through which a web is spun	The opening of a small bird's nest	Opening at the tip of a stamen					
11. Fauna	Collective for all the animal life in a region	Collective for all the plant life in a region	Collective for all the rock formations in a region					
12. Proboscis	Tubular part of the mouth	Tip of an insect's antenna	The fine hairs on the body of a spider					
Total								

DID YOU KNOW?

The sable antelope has an impressive set of swept-back horns that can kill the largest of predators.

Multiple choice quiz 6

Allocate each player a number and record his or her choice under
the relevant number. Check for the correct answers on page 54.

QUESTIONS	1	2	3	4	5
1. What type of animal is a mandrill? a) A fox b) A monkey c) A bird					
2. What can a chameleon do that other reptiles can't? a) Change colour b) Shed its skin c) Climb trees					
3. What kind of animal is a sole? a) A fish b) A bird c) An insect					
4. What do barracudas eat? a) Seaweed b) Prawns c) Other fish					
5. What is a gannet? a) A fish b) A bird c) An insect					
6. Which is the biggest fish in the world? a) Blue marlin b) Whale shark c) Dolphin					
7. What is the covering that protects a fish's gills called? a) Operculum b) Nictitating membrane c) Nostril					
8. What do fish use nostrils for? a) To breathe b) To smell c) To help them eat					
9. What do lungfish use nostrils for? a) To breathe b) To smell c) To help them eat					
10. Where do tilapia fish keep their eggs until they hatch? a) In a nest b) Attached to their bellies c) In their mouths					

Above table header: **PLAYERS**

DID YOU KNOW?

Wild dogs can communicate with
each other over a distance of 3 km!

QUESTIONS continued

	1	2	3	4	5
11. How fast can an ostrich run? a) 40 km per hour b) 50 km per hour c) 60 km per hour					
12. What are the claws of a bird of prey called? a) Talons b) Spurs c) Claws					
13. How many muscles does an elephant have in its trunk? a) 60 000 b) 80 000 c) 100 000					
14. The largest falcon in South Africa is the... ? a) Sooty falcon b) Peregrine falcon c) Lanner falcon					
15. How many ribs does a snake have? a) 200 b) 400 c) 600					
16. How does a python kill its prey? a) By constricting it b) By biting it c) By squirting venom in its eyes					
17. What do swans keep for life? a) Same nest b) Same mate c) Same feathers					
18. How many toes does a zebra have on each foot? a) 0 b) 1 c) 2					
19. Why do African elephants have big ears? a) To swat flies b) To keep cool c) To hear predators					
20. How long do worker bees live during the active season? a) 3 to 4 weeks b) 5 to 6 weeks c) 7 to 8 weeks					
Total					

DID YOU KNOW?

A group of peacocks is called a muster.

Crossword 4

Answers on p 54.

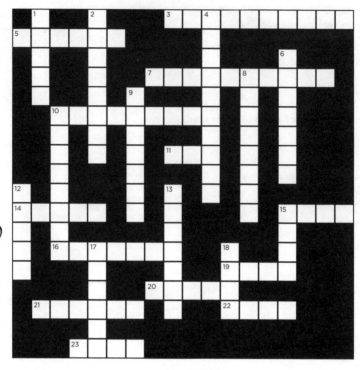

HINT!

Down 1:
Rodent, often caught by owls

Across

3 Pachyderm (10)

5 On or pertaining to the back (6)

7 Sound with a frequency too high for humans to hear (10)

10 The outermost flight feathers in a bird's wing (9)

11 Wildebeest (3)

14 Not native to a country or region (5)

15 A bee's home (4)

16 Largest primate (7)

19 The wax structure of cells built up by bees (4)

20 The external part of an ear (5)

21 Bare, fleshy, brightly coloured skin hanging loosely from a bird's neck or throat (6)

22 Small sea bird (4)

23 The portion of a bird's oesophagus in which food is stored (4)

Down

1 Rodent, often caught by owls (5)

2 An animal that feeds off another living animal, causing it harm (8)

4 Sound with a frequency too low for humans to hear (10)

6 The central kernel of a nut or seed (7)

8 Distinctively coloured area on the wing of certain birds (8)

9 The process in which a first-hatched chick kills its siblings (7)

10 Birds keep their feathers waterproof by ... (8)

12 A group of females guarded by a male who retains mating rights (5)

13 A word pertaining to birds that spend most of their lives out at sea (7)

15 Plant often used in cooking and traditional medicines (4)

17 A bird or prey (6)

18 A carnivore's faeces (4)

Quiz 4

Ask each player the same question and record their answers on a separate sheet of paper. Record their scores (✔ or ✗) in the spaces provided.
The correct answers are on page 55.

QUESTIONS	PLAYERS				
	1	2	3	4	5
1. During which season of the year do swallows come to South Africa?					
2. Which animal appears on the jerseys of the South African rugby team?					
3. What is the fastest land animal?					
4. Does the male or female cricket make the chirping sound?					
5. What is another name for perlemoen?					
6. Which animal squirts black ink to escape from danger?					
7. Why does a firefly emit a flashing light in the dark?					
8. Which has the longer snout – a crocodile or an alligator?					
9. Do some elephants live in the desert?					
10. Why is the dodo famous?					
11. Are termites ants?					
12. Which elephants have bigger ears – African or Indian?					
13. What do we call people who study plants?					
14. What is a male elephant called?					
15. Which mammal lives in a pride?					
16. Which has more legs – a millipede or a centipede?					
17. Where is a scorpion's sting located?					
18. What's the difference between a dolphin and a porpoise?					
19. What is the Egyptian cobra unable to do that many other cobras can do?					
20. Which animal has the longest neck?					
Total					

DID YOU KNOW?
An aardvark's sticky tongue can extend for 30 cm.

Multiple choice quiz 7

Allocate each player a number and record his or her choice under
the relevant number. Check for the correct answers on page 55.

QUESTIONS	PLAYERS				
	1	2	3	4	5
1. Which animal sleeps standing up? a) A mountain goat b) A Flamingo c) An Ostrich					
2. What is the average life span of a butterfly? a) 1 to 2 weeks b) 3 to 4 weeks c) 5 to 6 weeks					
3. What age can hippos live to in the wild? a) 25 b) 45 c) 65					
4. The giraffe has ... bones in its neck, as many as humans do. a) 3 b) 5 c) 7					
5. What is the lifespan of a queen bee? a) 1 year b) 2 years c) 5 years					
6. What do you call a group of leopards? a) A leap b) A pack c) A pride					
7. Which mammals have the largest eyes? a) Humans b) Giraffes c) Lions					
8. Which animal spends its entire adult life in one place? a) A barnacle b) A mussel c) A dung beetle					
9. Which one does not live on another animal's blood? a) Dust mite b) Flea c) Vampire bat					
10. To which group do dolphins belong? a) Mammals b) Crustaceans c) Fishes					

DID YOU KNOW?

The springbok can jump as high as 3 m!
That is nearly the height of an elephant.

QUESTIONS continued

	1	2	3	4	5

11. Which is the loudest noise made by an animal?
a) A lion's roar
b) A blue whale's 'song'
c) A dog's bark

12. As soon as a warthog senses trouble it ...
a) goes into hiding
b) sticks its tail straight up in the air like an aerial
c) grunts to attract the attention of other animals

13. Which animal is the fastest swimmer?
a) A shark
b) A whale
c) A dolphin

14. What percentage of bees in a colony may be workers?
a) 60%
b) 90%
c) 98%

15. How would you describe a crow's call?
a) A caw
b) A whistle
c) A screech

16. When are hedgehogs most active?
a) During the day
b) At night
c) Early in the morning

17. Predators' eyes are generally...
a) on top of their heads
b) forward-looking
c) sideways-looking

18. Which is the only cat to live in a family group?
a) A lion
b) A cheetah
c) A leopard

19. Why do snakes continually flick out their tongues?
a) To taste
b) To threaten other animals
c) To smell

20. What are fossorial animals?
a) Fossilised animals
b) Digging or burrowing animals
c) Types of fish

Total

DID YOU KNOW?
Honey badgers will climb trees if necessary to reach the honey.

Which tree am I?

Read the following descriptions of African trees one at a time and ask each player to identify what has been described. Allow them 20 seconds to answer. Check for the correct answers on page 55 and record the players' scores in the space provided. If they don't answer in time they miss the round.

CLUES	PLAYERS				
	1	2	3	4	5
1. I grow in Mpumalanga and have a large, heavy, sausage-like seedpod. My wood is used to make dugout canoes.					
2. I am fairly common tree in KwaZulu-Natal and Mpumalanga. I have white or pink blossoms that look like pear blossoms. These are amongst the first spring flowers. I have rough, very dark, thick bark.					
3. I grow in the Limpopo Province and northern Mpumalanga. I have a large trunk with small branches and I look like I grow upside down. My fruit is rich in tartaric acid and I am protected by law.					
4. I have butterfly-shaped leaves that smell of turpentine if crushed. A large caterpillar-like worm that shares my name feeds on me. My hard wood is dark red and is used for railway sleepers and fencing.					
5. I bear yellow, plum-like fruit that is enjoyed by elephants, monkeys, and baboons. My fruit is used to make alcohol and medicine. I can grow up to 10 m high.					
6. I grow along the coastal area between Cape Town and Port Elizabeth. My soft, light wood was used for wagon yokes.					
7. I have many bright red flowers in winter. My black and red seeds are poisonous. My soft white wood was used for brake blocks on wagons.					
8. I grow along the coast eastwards of Cape Town. I am a low, gnarled evergreen with unpleasant smelling white flowers and bad tasting fruit but I am protected by law.					
Total					

DID YOU KNOW?

The rooikrans is an invader tree that is not indigenous to South Africa. It grows naturally in eastern Australia.

Wordsearch

Find the trees and shrubs

The names of 24 different trees and shrubs are hidden horizontally and vertically in the grid below. Draw a circle around each one and record it on the list. The first one has been found for you. Why not make a photocopy of the grid for each of the players? Ask someone to time you and see who can find all the answers first. The answer grid is on page 55.

A	Z	B	O	T	T	L	E	B	R	U	S	H	D	R	Y	C	H	E	S	T	N	U	T	D
B	I	U	Y	T	R	Q	E	I	U	Y	L	H	T	E	U	Y	R	B	N	Y	M	E	R	D
U	E	R	C	A	M	P	H	O	R	X	K	Y	A	D	E	R	H	J	D	D	Y	I	U	M
F	R	H	J	H	U	Y	R	B	N	C	J	E	M	P	I	U	Y	T	R	Q	E	D	R	E
F	U	C	T	C	E	R	H	J	D	Y	F	Z	B	U	Y	A	S	H	H	J	D	O	H	B
A	R	O	N	L	I	B	Y	T	R	C	D	R	O	R	B	N	Z	C	A	J	A	G	A	O
L	H	R	D	U	Y	L	E	R	H	A	A	R	T	Z	D	E	R	H	J	D	D	W	H	N
O	R	K	J	S	B	U	Z	C	A	D	V	O	I	R	B	A	O	B	A	B	R	O	J	Y
T	U	W	T	T	D	E	R	H	J	D	H	J	U	Y	R	H	J	U	Y	R	U	O	T	U
H	R	O	N	E	R	B	J	H	O	N	E	Y	S	U	C	K	L	E	I	O	R	D	N	R
O	H	O	D	R	U	U	T	R	H	J	I	O	P	I	U	Y	R	B	N	Y	H	J	D	H
R	R	D	J	L	R	S	N	U	Y	T	A	L	O	E	E	R	H	J	A	C	A	C	I	A
N	U	Y	T	E	H	H	D	R	B	N	D	R	Y	U	O	D	Q	H	J	S	U	Y	T	U
Y	R	B	N	A	R	H	J	E	T	R	U	I	M	O	P	A	N	E	T	N	B	I	O	P
B	H	J	D	F	U	Y	T	L	N	U	Y	C	F	G	T	Y	O	B	N	F	E	V	E	R
J	R	H	J	H	J	A	L	D	E	R	O	O	C	C	V	O	P	R	Y	U	E	R	Y	U
H	U	Y	T	Y	T	T	R	E	R	H	J	R	O	R	H	J	A	I	O	P	C	I	O	P
Y	R	B	N	B	N	N	U	R	U	Y	T	A	R	U	Y	T	N	D	F	G	H	D	F	G
B	E	U	G	E	N	I	A	Z	R	M	I	L	K	W	O	O	D	Z	X	C	Y	Z	X	C

- ☑ Acacia
- ☐ Alder
- ☐ Aloe
- ☐ Ash
- ☐ Baobab
- ☐ Beech
- ☐ Bluebush
- ☐ Bottlebrush
- ☐ Buffalo thorn
- ☐ Camphor
- ☐ Chestnut
- ☐ Clusterleaf
- ☐ Coral
- ☐ Corkwood
- ☐ Cycad
- ☐ Dogwood
- ☐ Ebony
- ☐ Elder
- ☐ Eugenia
- ☐ Fever
- ☐ Honeysuckle
- ☐ Mopane
- ☐ Milkwood
- ☐ Tamboti

DID YOU KNOW?

Because of its size the adult male roan antelope has very few enemies and only lions can prey on them.

35

Multiple choice quiz 8

Allocate each player a number and record his or her choice under
the relevant number. Check for the correct answers on page 55.

QUESTIONS	PLAYERS				
	1	2	3	4	5
1. How many pairs of legs do bees have? a) 6 b) 2 c) 3					
2. Which animal has an oval-shaped track with lobes at the front and sides? a) An elephant b) A rhino c) An impala					
3. How long can elephants live? a) 20 years b) 70 years c) 90 years					
4. What does a daisy do in overcast weather? a) Opens up b) Drops its petals c) Remains closed					
5. Which bird protects its eggs by making a false nest entrance? a) The Cape penduline tit b) The cormorant c) The cuckoo					
6. Which doesn't live in a monogamous pair? a) A swan b) A red fox c) An aardwolf					
7. How many eyelids do snakes have? a) 4 b) 2 c) None					
8. What distance can an impala leap? a) 10 m b) 14 m c) 16 m					
9. How many honey bees normally live in an average colony? a) 20 000 b) 40 000 c) 60 000					
10. What is the main colour inside a pear limpet (a type of shell)? a) Blue b) Pink c) Violet					

DID YOU KNOW?
Many old African transport roads
were originally elephants' paths.

QUESTIONS continued

11. From what distance can the male emperor moth smell a female?
a) 1 km
b) 1,2 km
c) 1,5 km

12. How many eggs does a housefly lay in one batch?
a) 150
b) 300
c) 450

13. What is the approximate weight of an elephant's heart?
a) Approximately 7 kg
b) Approximately 15 kg
c) Approximately 24 kg

14. To what depth can a sperm whale dive?
a) 2 000 m
b) 3 000 m
c) 4 000 m

15. How many legs does an earthworm have?
a) None
b) 100
c) 1 000

16. How much water does a rhino drink in a day?
a) 100 litres
b) 200 litres
c) 300 litres

17. How many arms do most starfish have?
a) 4
b) 5
c) 6

18. How many pairs of wings does a bee have?
a) 2
b) 4
c) 6

19. What type of eyes do flies have?
a) Simple
b) Compound
c) Multiple

20. What is the speed of a charging elephant?
a) 40 km per hour
b) 60 km per hour
c) 80 km per hour

Total

DID YOU KNOW?
A Cape sparrow has to eat its body mass in seeds and insects everyday.

What's that word? 4

Ask each player to identify the meaning of the following words and record their answers in the spaces provided. Check the correct answers on page 55.

WORD	A	B	C	PLAYERS 1	2	3	4	5
1. Saltatorial	Living in salt water	Adapted for a leaping, bounding locomotion	Superior					
2. Drongo	A bird that feeds on honeybees	The sound made by a sugarbird	The reverberation from a lion's roar					
3. Detritus	A herd of wild pigs	Debris or material that has disintegrated	A common disease in wild animals					
4. Drupe	A fruit containing a single stone or pip	To hang loosely	The cover on a chameleon's eye					
5. Terrestrial	Marked out territory	Avoiding water	Living on land					
6. Glaucous	Covered with a powdery, whitish bloom	The shape of a seagull's beak	The long bone in the hind leg of a sable					
7. Albinism	Pretending to be dead	A deficiency of pigment in the hair, skin, or eyes	The coating on an oyster shell					
8. Endemic	A deadly disease	Something occurring only in a specified area	Something that is passed on genetically					
9. Enzootic	A disease occurring in a given species within a specific area	The fluid between the bones in a joint	Able to turn in all directions					
10. Pandemic	Epidemic in a specific, narrow geographical area	Epidemic over a wide geographical area, existing everywhere	Epidemic that spans continents					
11. Insect-ivorous	Feeding on insects	Shaped like an insect	Flesh-eating insects					
12. Lamella	The hard shell of a scorpion	The lid of a mussel shell	Spore-bearing gill of a mushroom					
Total								

Lion quiz

Ask each player the same question and record their answers on a separate sheet of paper. Record their scores (✔ or ✗) in the spaces provided. The correct answers are on page 55.

QUESTIONS	PLAYERS				
	1	2	3	4	5
1. What is the common name for *Panthera leo*?					
2. How tall are adult male lions at the shoulder?					
3. How many lion cubs may be born in the same litter?					
4. At what age are the cubs introduced to the pride?					
5. What is the average lifespan of a lion?					
6. By what age do male lions leave the pride?					
7. Do lionesses suckle the cubs of other lionesses?					
8. What is the average weight of a newborn lion cub?					
9. For how many hours per day are lions active?					
10. What is the weight of the average daily intake of food for an adult male lion?					
Total					

DID YOU KNOW?

Giraffe bulls have been known to knock each other out during fights.

True or false? 2

Some of the following statements are true and some are false. Record each person's answers (T or F) in the spaces provided and check the correct answers on page 55.

STATEMENTS	PLAYERS				
	1	2	3	4	5
1. A tsetse fly cannot bite.					
2. A fish uses its nostrils to breathe in air.					
3. Tadpoles grow up to be frogs.					
4. Pythons kill their prey by biting them.					
5. Crocodiles don't live in rivers.					
6. Cockroaches are classified as beetles.					
7. Sea turtles have legs.					
8. Snowy owls are indigenous to Africa.					
9. Most swallows return to the same nest each summer.					
10. Butterflies migrate.					
11. Sharks have no colour vision.					
12. Adult tortoises have teeth.					
13. If a whale gets stranded on a beach its own weight can crush it.					
14. Only the male black widow spider can bite.					
15. A hermit crab has a shell on its back					
Total					

DID YOU KNOW?

The ostrich is the only African bird that leaves a two-toed track.

Antelope & wildebeest quiz

Ask each player the same question and record their answers on a separate sheet of paper. Record their scores (✔ or ✗) in the spaces provided. The correct answers are on page 55.

QUESTIONS	PLAYERS				
	1	2	3	4	5
1. Which is the largest antelope in South Africa?					
2. Which wildebeest has horns that first grow downward and then upwards?					
3. What is the top speed of a red hartebeest?					
4. Which antelope is one of the fastest and most enduring runners, giving it a name that means 'tough ox'?					
5. What is the preferred diet of the blue duiker?					
6. What is the stiff-legged jumping of a springbok called?					
7. Which sex of grysbok has horns?					
8. At what age do female impala give birth for the first time?					
9. How tall are adult male roan antelope at the shoulder?					
10. What colour are the upper parts of an adult sable antelope bull?					
Total					

DID YOU KNOW?
A kick from a giraffe can kill a lion.

True or false? 3

Some of the following statements are true and some are false. Record each person's answers (T or F) in the spaces provided and check the correct answers on page 56.

STATEMENTS	PLAYERS				
	1	2	3	4	5
1. An octopus swims by sucking in water and then forcing it out.					
2. The male gorilla is known as a bull.					
3. The male cricket makes the chirping sound.					
4. The blind fly is known by this name because it cannot see.					
5. Giraffes can run as fast as racehorses.					
6. Lions carry their prey up trees.					
7. A mongoose often kills and eats snakes.					
8. The honey badger does not eat honey.					
9. Porcupines attack by running backwards.					
10. Camels carry water in their humps.					
11. Bats hang upside down when resting.					
12. Troops of baboons have a ranking system.					
13. The blue whale is the largest mammal.					
14. Mammals are cold-blooded.					
15. Bearded vultures drop bones from a height onto a flat rock to split them open to get to the marrow.					
Total					

DID YOU KNOW?

African dung beetles are so good at burying dung quickly that they are exported to Australia to help curb the problem they have in that country with ground-breeding flies that breed in dung.

Insect quiz

Ask each player the same question and record their answers on a separate sheet of paper. Record their scores (✔ or ✘) in the spaces provided. The correct answers are on page 56.

QUESTIONS	PLAYERS				
	1	2	3	4	5
1. Which bone is missing in an insect?					
2. What is the tough, outer casing on the body of an insect called?					
3. Which flying insect feeds on aphids?					
4. How many hopper stages does a brown locust go through?					
5. What is another name for insects?					
6. How many times its own length can a cat flea leap?					
7. What is the feeding tube of a butterfly or moth called?					
8. Which insect regularly lays eggs in the flesh of living sheep?					
9. What colour are the eyes of a horsefly?					
10. What is the egg-laying tube of most female insects called?					
Total					

DID YOU KNOW?
The wingless female bladder grasshopper is unable to fly or jump.

True or false? 4

Some of the following statements are true and some are false. Record each person's answers (T or F) in the spaces provided and check the correct answers on page 56.

STATEMENTS	PLAYERS				
	1	2	3	4	5
1. A gecko's tail can break off and then grow back.					
2. Fossorial animals are digging or burrowing animals.					
3. Pythons cannot climb trees.					
4. Some lions are white.					
5. Some camels have one hump.					
6. True eagles do not have feathers on their legs.					
7. The white rhino is more dangerous than the black.					
8. Elephants can't see far.					
9. Some scorprions can squirt their venom.					
10. A baboon spider bite is not dangerous to humans.					
11. Seals have external ears.					
12. Whales can't communicate with each other.					
13. The water spider lives in water.					
14. Hippos are very dangerous.					
15. Bats cannot fly in the dark.					
Total					

DID YOU KNOW?

Giraffes can eat the leaves of thorn trees without hurting themselves.

Spider quiz

Ask each player the same question and record their answers on a separate sheet of paper. Record their scores (✔ or ✘) in the spaces provided. The correct answers are on page 56.

QUESTIONS	PLAYERS				
	1	2	3	4	5
1. What is the row of curved, serrated bristles on the foot of the fourth leg of a spider called?					
2. What are the hair-like bristles that cover a spider called?					
3. What are the organs that spin spider silk called?					
4. Name the venom that affects the nervous system.					
5. What are the second set of 'claws' on a spider's cephalothorax called?					
6. Which hairy South African spider is among the world's largest?					
7. How many eyes do most spiders have?					
8. On a spider, what are the claws used for biting, chewing and grasping called?					
9. The female of which species of spider frequently kills the male after mating?					
10. On what part of the spider's body are the spinnerets located?					
Total					

DID YOU KNOW?
Button spiders are the most poisonous group of spiders in South Africa.

True or false? 5

Some of the following statements are true and some are false. Record each person's answers (T or F) in the spaces provided and check the correct answers on page 56.

STATEMENTS	PLAYERS				
	1	2	3	4	5
1. Bats are blind.					
2. Special family groups exist in baboon troops.					
3. Sharks have a skeleton.					
4. A cheetah's claws are permanently exposed.					
5. Female rhinos can't kick.					
6. Puffadders lay eggs.					
7. The leaves of a common poison bush kill cattle that eat them.					
8. A snake can be tamed in captivity.					
9. An octopus can shoot out black ink when trying to escape.					
10. A floodplain viper is strictly terrestrial.					
11. Sharks have very good vision.					
12. The fox's hearing is so sensitive that it can pinpoint its prey underground.					
13. Up to 90 baby scorpions can ride on their mother's back at a time.					
14. A falcon will only kill for food.					
15. Sharks can't smell.					
Total					

DID YOU KNOW?
The light creamy colour of the Ostrich's egg keeps it from overheating in the hot southern African sun.

Elephant quiz

Ask each player the same question and record their answers on a separate sheet of paper. Record their scores (✔ or ✗) in the spaces provided. The correct answers are on page 56.

The correct answers are on page 56.

QUESTIONS	PLAYERS				
	1	2	3	4	5
1. On average, how tall are adult bull elephants at the shoulder?					
2. What is the average weight of an adult bull elephant?					
3. What was the weight of the heaviest tusks ever recorded?					
4. How is the height of an elephant estimated?					
5. What is the average birth weight of an elephant calf?					
6. At what age are elephants weaned?					
7. What is the potential lifespan of an elephant?					
8. What is the most common cause of violent death amongst elephants?					
9. What is the average daily amount of water drunk by an adult bull elephant?					
10. How much blood is cooled in an elephant's ears per minute?					
Total					

DID YOU KNOW?

Kudus can easily jump over 2-m-high game fences and as a result they cause many fatal road accidents.

Quiz 5

Ask each player the same question and record their answers on a separate sheet of paper. Record their scores (✔ or ✘) in the spaces provided. The correct answers are on page 56.

QUESTIONS	PLAYERS				
	1	2	3	4	5
1. What is the name for a bee's home?					
2. Which feared African fly transmits 'sleeping sickness' or trypanosomiasis?					
3. Which bird is found only in fynbos of the Western Cape?					
4. How many toes do most birds have on each foot?					
5. What group do crabs fall into?					
6. What is another name for a bird called a griffon?					
7. What markings does a cheetah have?					
8. How many horns does a white rhinoceros have?					
9. Which amphibian makes a loud call similar to that of a calf?					
10. What does an aardvark eat?					
11. Name two African birds that cannot fly.					
12. What is an albatross?					
13. How many tentacles does an octopus have?					
14 Which part of a jellyfish stings people?					
15. What is a cod?					
16. What does endemic mean?					
17. When do lions do most of their hunting?					
18. Which fish is described as a 'living fossil'?					
19. What are the large, tooth-like objects sticking out on either side of a warthog's mouth?					
20. What is the hair around a male lion's head called?					
Total					

DID YOU KNOW?

White and black rhinoceroses are actually both grey in colour. The word 'white' in the first case is a corruption of the Afrikaans word 'wyd' for 'wide', which refers to the animal's broad, squarish mouth.

What's that word? 5

Ask each player to identify the meaning of the following words and record their answers in the spaces provided. Check the correct answers on page 56.

WORD	A	B	C	PLAYERS 1	2	3	4	5
1. Migratory	Remaining in one region all year round	Moving with the seasons from region to region	Nomadic					
2. Tuber	The seed pod of the sausage tree	Underground stem or root	The shape of the nest of a Red Bishop					
3. Propolis	Resinous material used by bees to waterproof and insulate the hive	The motion of the dorsal fin of a shark	The foam that binds the dung of an elephant					
4. Piscatory	The curved shape of a snake's fangs	Relating to fish	The jagged edge of a crocodile's tail					
5. Apiary	The den of a group of suricates	A group of bee hives	A common dung heap					
6. Ebb	The up and down motion of a warthog's tail	The centre of the pad on the front legs of an elephant	The movement of the tide out to sea					
7. Bullrush	Waterside plant with a long brown head	A stampede of angry buffalo	A water-based weed					
8. Passerine	Birds having feet adapted for perching	Found on the banks of a river	Medium-sized bird of prey					
9. Prehensile	Capable of grasping	The lack of ability to think lucidly	The twisting ability of a giraffe's neck					
10. Stridulation	The ridges found across a flat plain	The measured stride made by elephants	The sound some insects make by rubbing the wings or legs together					
11. Muzzle	The area between the claws of a hawk	The nose or mouth of an animal	The weathering action of a river					
12. Ecru	An antelope from the Namib desert	The mane on an eland bull	A light beige or cream colour					
Total								

DID YOU KNOW?

The back of the blade of a knife should be used to scrape away the sting of a bee left in the victim's skin.

Wordsearch

Find the fish

The names of 25 different fish are hidden horizontally and vertically in the grid below. Draw a circle around each one and record it on the list. The first one has been found for you. Why not make a photocopy of the grid for each of the players? Ask someone to time you and see who can find all the answers first. The answer grid is on page 56.

```
S P R I N G E R B N B B R E A M B N B N D B G B S
U Y R B N Y T Z J D J T E R H T J D J D O J U J T
G R U N T E R Z T R T X S N A P P E R X G T R T I
I U Y T R E R B A S S U Y R B N Y T U Y F R N R N
Y T E R H L U B N B E E R H S H A R K R I B A B G
T R Q E I T R J D J A I U Y T R Q R I U S B R B R
A N C H O V Y T R T H Y T E R H J U Y T H J D J A
Y T Y V E U R B E O U Y R B N Y T U Y S T R T Y
E R E R D E R H J D R E R H J D D R E R P R H R U
Y S N O E K E U Y R S E U Y R B C A T F I S H Y T
H Y T C O P D E R H E D E R H J T E R H T E R H T
E E R K F G E U Y R T E R H T S A N D S H A R K H
R R B C A S T E E N B R A S D S F B N E A S D F G
R Y T O E U Y R B E U Y R B E R O M A N N B C O D
I E R D D E R H J D E R H J D E G T R E R B N Y T
N R H J R H A M M E R H E A D T U R H N H J D D R
G U Y T U R H J R H J E V R H J R P I L C H A R D
T T E R T U Y T U Y T R C U Y T N B N Y E R H J G
S E V E N T Y F O U R R K T E R S T U M P N O S E
```

☑ Anchovy
☐ Bass
☐ Bream
☐ Catfish
☐ Cod
☐ Dogfish
☐ Eel

☐ Grunter
☐ Gurnard
☐ Hammerhead
☐ Herring
☐ Pilchard
☐ Rockcod
☐ Roman

☐ Sand shark
☐ Seahorse
☐ Seventyfour
☐ Shark
☐ Snapper
☐ Snoek
☐ Springer

☐ Steenbras
☐ Stingray
☐ Stumpnose

DID YOU KNOW?
The serval is very agile and can leap up high enough to catch birds in flight.

Which reptile am I?

Read the following descriptions of African reptiles one at a time and ask each player to identify what has been described. Allow them 20 seconds to answer. Check for the correct answers on page 56 and record the players' scores in the space provided. If they don't answer in time they miss the round.

CLUES	PLAYERS				
	1	2	3	4	5
1. I live in the rivers and swamps of the northern parts of KwaZulu-Natal and Mpumalanga. I may reach a length of 6 m.					
2. I live throughout the subtropical areas of South Africa and grow to about 20 cm or longer. When alarmed, I can inflate my body and make a hissing sound. I can change colour.					
3. I am a harmless snake and am often found in houses.					
4. I am the largest tortoise in southern Africa and have markings similar to one of the big cats.					
5. I can often be seen clinging to the walls with the pads on my feet. I eat insects and clean my eyes using my tongue.					
6. I am mostly brownish-black with an olive-green underside. I occur mainly in KwaZulu-Natal and parts of the North West province. I am extremely poisonous! I move swiftly through trees and bush.					
7. I am widespread except in the drier parts. My mouth is small and I am reluctant to bite but I am very venomous. I move swiftly through trees and bush.					
8. I can grown to be 6 m in length. I am not venomous but a bite from me will become badly infected. I live mainly in KwaZulu-Natal and north of the Vaal river.					
Total					

> **DID YOU KNOW?**
> Secretions from the scent glands of a civet are used in the manufacture of expensive perfumes.

Answers

QUIZ 1 (p. 3)

1. an antelope **2.** Addo Elephant Park **3.** black widow/button spider **4.** amphibians **5.** the hippopotamus **6.** autumn **7.** an elephant **8.** rock rabbit/dassie **9.** the anthers **10.** female **11.** bat-eared fox **12.** a waterbird **13.** Kruger National Park **14.** locusts **15.** pretends to be dead **16.** the tsessebe **17.** laughs/mad laughter **18.** a vixen **19.** a troop **20.** a moth

WORDSEARCH: FIND THE 'CREEPY-CRAWLIES' (p. 4)

A	P	H	I	D	G	T	B	G	T	B	G	C	E	N	T	I	P	E	D	E	C	V	C	C
C	V	R	T	Y	G	T	B	G	T	B	G	I	Z	U	E	P	Z	U	O	P	R	E	R	O
R	E	S	T	I	N	K	B	U	G	G	T	C	U	H	R	R	X	E	S	T	M	A	N	C
E	E	T	G	E	B	E	E	T	L	E	V	D	O	E	I	Z	G	L	T	O	E	T	Z	R
F	O	I	T	V	A	R	G	T	B	G	T	A	M	T	T	W	X	Y	A	M	T	H	W	O
L	O	C	E	Z	G	L	G	T	B	G	T	V	O	S	E	V	A	R	M	O	S	W	V	A
E	M	K	D	W	X	Y	M	O	S	Q	U	I	T	O	U	O	P	U	P	O	E	O	Z	C
A	O	S	G	V	A	R	U	O	P	Z	U	O	P	Z	P	Z	X	P	A	M	T	R	W	H
U	O	P	R	U	O	T	P	Z	I	P	O	R	E	D	R	O	M	A	N	O	S	M	V	S
D	Z	X	A	P	Z	G	G	T	D	O	S	T	V	A	R	O	S	T	R	O	E	E	Z	M
R	T	E	S	G	T	W	C	V	E	O	E	E	Z	G	L	O	E	C	R	S	C	K	E	I
A	V	B	S	C	V	E	R	E	R	M	F	I	S	H	M	O	T	H	O	C	U	O	P	L
G	E	D	H	R	E	E	A	G	X	O	S	T	V	A	R	O	S	P	Z	O	P	Z	X	L
O	S	T	O	A	G	V	Z	D	A	M	S	E	L	F	L	Y	K	G	T	R	G	T	E	I
N	E	E	P	Z	E	I	U	O	P	I	U	O	P	G	T	B	G	C	V	P	C	V	B	P
F	T	D	P	U	O	L	P	Z	X	T	P	F	I	R	E	F	L	Y	E	I	R	E	D	E
L	S	T	E	P	Z	A	G	T	E	E	G	T	E	U	O	P	U	A	G	O	A	G	F	D
Y	E	E	R	G	T	B	C	V	B	F	C	R	I	C	K	E	T	Z	E	N	Z	E	U	E

TRUE OR FALSE? 1 (p. 5)

1. T **2.** F **3.** T **4.** T **5.** F **6.** F **7.** T **8.** T **9.** T **10.** F **11.** T **12.** T **13.** T **14.** T **15.** T

WHAT'S THAT WORD? 1 (p. 6):

1. B **2.** B **3.** B **4.** B **5.** A **6.** B **7.** B **8.** C **9.** A **10.** B **11.** A **12.** B

CROSSWORD 1 (p. 7):

ACROSS: **3.** sharks **5.** cuckoo **7.** squid **8.** spat **9.** Southern Cross **12.** Beak **13.** centipede **15.** warthogs **19.** owls **21.** dolphin **23.** ozone **24.** eel **25.** aloe **26.** bat
DOWN: **1.** body heat **2.** pod **4.** reptiles **6.** burchells **10.** ostrich **11.** death cap **12.** beat **14.** whale **16.** hooves **17.** sponges **18.** fynbos **20.** mole **21.** den **22.** limpet

MULTIPLE CHOICE QUIZ 1 (p. 8):

1. a: A reptile **2.** a: A flower **3.** b: Occurring naturally in an area **4.** a: A flower **5.** b: Field mushroom **6.** a: A clan **7.** a: A cat **8.** b: White **9.** a: The study of birds' eggs **10.** a: An animal **11.** b: Through their mouths **12.** c: Neither A nor B **13.** c: Bats **14.** a: Upper **15.** a: Dorsal fin **16.** c: A guard bee **17.** a: Eland **18.** a: Active during daylight **19.** c: It hits the crab against a rock **20.** c: Compressed hair

QUIZ 2 (p. 10)

1. the blue duiker **2.** yellow **3.** a bird **4.** they beat it to death on their perch **5.** the white circle around its rump **6.** its hammer-shaped head **7.** black and white 8. regurgitate water from her stomach and spray it on her calf **9.** brown **10.** no **11.** active during the twilight hours **12.** a calf **13.** World Wide Fund (for Nature) **14.** Australia **15.** tree ferns **16.** a lynx **17.** backwards **18.** both male & female **19.** traditional medicine **20.** shoal

WHAT'S THAT WORD? 2 (p. 11):

1. B **2.** B **3.** C **4.** A **5.** C **6.** C **7.** A **8.** B **9.** B **10.** A **11.** B **12.** A

MULTIPLE CHOICE QUIZ 2 (p. 12)
1. b: Shepherd's tree **2.** a: Nervous system **3.** a: Spores **4.** b: Backwards **5.** a: the vascular system **6.** b: Stonefish **7.** c: Snow white **8.** c: A fern **9.** c: A lizard **10.** c: Tannin **11.** b: Puffadder **12.** a: The male **13.** b: Plants using the sun's energy to produce food **14.** a: Animals **15.** b: Behind the last pair of legs **16.** b: A porcupine **17.** a: Alpha male **18.** c: Both sexes **19.** a: White **20.** c: The African rock python

CROSSWORD 2 (p. 14):
ACROSS: **2.** hibernate **5.** fangs **6.** crocodile **8.** abdomen **11.** wagtail **13.** camouflage **16.** fungi **17.** baboon **20.** cannibals **21.** fossil **23.** metamorphosis
DOWN: **1.** algae **3.** barracuda **4.** cell **7.** mating **9.** drone **10.** migration **12.** amphibian **13.** caterpillar **14.** grub **15.** cocoon **18.** moulting **19.** host **22.** roe

QUIZ 3 (p. 15)
1. green **2.** nagapie **3.** female reproduction without mating **4.** a dry bite **5.** a chameleon **6.** a pelican **7.** puffadders **8.** yes **9.** they don't like the taste **10.** through the underside **11.** to allow them to grow larger/ their skin is not elastic **12.** a mermaid's purse **13.** molluscs **14.** a foal **15.** mosquitoes (through malaria) **16.** lungs **17.** without wings **18.** a flower **19.** the baobab **20.** a radula

MULTIPLE CHOICE QUIZ 3 (p. 16)
1. c: Cold water **2.** a: Teeth **3.** b: Cold-blooded **4.** a: White mussel **5.** b: Vertebrae **6.** c: Both A & B **7.** b: Carnivorous **8.** c: the horny plate on the shell of a tortoise **9.** a: breed in dung. **10.** c: A colony **11.** c: A caracal **12.** a: Across their legs **13.** b: locate their prey. **14.** c: Chlorophyll **15.** c: Flowers and cones **16.** c: 8 **17.** a: Salt water **18.** a: Through their roots **19.** a: Pink prawn **20.** c: snake.

WHICH ANIMAL AM I? (p. 18):
1. Giraffe **2.** Black rhino **3.** Black wildebeest **4.** Buffalo **5.** Leopard **6.** Aardvark **7.** Dassie **8.** Bat-eared fox

WORDSEARCH: FIND THE BIRDS (p. 19)

S	E	C	R	E	T	A	R	Y	B	I	R	D	Z	S	D	R	Y	U	O	P	G	U	L	L
A	S	D	F	G	H	J	K	L	Q	W	E	R	T	Y	U	I	O	P	Z	X	C	V	B	N
B	N	P	E	N	G	U	I	N	H	J	K	L	Q	D	Y	D	F	G	T	E	F	S	F	D
S	H	E	Z	X	C	V	B	N	S	D	R	Y	U	A	O	Z	X	C	V	B	N	H	Y	A
E	R	T	M	N	B	V	C	X	A	L	B	A	T	R	O	S	S	R	E	D	T	E	O	B
T	Y	R	S	R	Y	E	O	S	T	V	A	R	Q	T	S	A	S	A	G	F	Y	R	M	C
G	N	E	E	L	Y	G	O	E	E	Z	G	L	I	E	E	V	X	Z	E	U	U	O	C	H
D	M	L	T	Y	R	M	T	D	W	X	Y	P	R	T	P	E	L	I	C	A	N	J	I	
A	A	D	D	G	G	E	Z	X	E	M	O	E	U	Y	R	B	N	Y	M	Z	A	W	B	C
T	E	R	N	P	Q	T	V	N	Y	J	S	D	E	P	L	O	V	E	R	J	K	X	V	K
A	S	D	F	H	H	G	J	K	L	O	T	P	I	U	Y	T	R	Q	E	W	I	M	B	G
Q	U	A	I	L	O	K	L	S	T	O	R	K	X	S	W	S	P	O	O	N	B	I	L	L
H	Q	R	W	T	R	I	P	Y	J	M	I	T	I	P	S	S	P	W	B	T	I	R	N	K
A	A	G	O	O	S	E	K	E	R	Q	C	G	J	K	E	T	I	T	S	S	S	F	B	M
D	Z	V	X	B	D	H	N	B	F	A	H	B	M	M	R	C	D	Z	R	W	G	B	V	W
U	Q	Q	F	L	A	M	I	N	G	O	Z	X	C	V	G	U	I	N	E	A	F	O	W	L
C	S	D	F	H	B	E	U	Y	R	B	N	Y	M	T	E	U	Y	R	B	N	Y	M	W	U
K	K	J	U	I	C	D	E	R	H	A	V	O	C	E	T	E	R	H	J	D	D	Y	A	S
O	F	R	A	N	C	O	L	I	N	T	R	Q	E	O	P	I	H	A	M	E	R	K	O	P

MULTIPLE CHOICE QUIZ 4 (p. 20)
1. a: Ivory **2.** a: An otter **3.** b: A lion **4.** b: 22 months **5.** b: A sett **6.** a: Its tail **7.** a: The Cape fur seal **8.** c: Their blubber (fat) **9.** c: Sonar **10.** a: flying foxes. **11.** b: Females **12.** c: Both jaws **13.** b: 2nd dorsal fin **14.** a: Killer whale **15.** b: twice **16.** a: River horse **17.** b: The king cheetah has stripes. **18.** a: Their canine teeth are too short. **19.** a: Their sweat acts as a sunscreen **20.** c: to signal that it has found food.

CROSSWORD 3 (p. 22):
ACROSS: **3.** sap **4.** doves **7.** culmen **8.** dewlap **10.** eagle **12.** midrib **17.** workers **18.** reeds **20.** web **21.** succulent **22.** amoeba **23.** herbaceous **25.** ibis **26.** sting
DOWN: **1.** pollen **2.** sepal **3.** snare **5.** queen **6.** nectar **9.** apiary **11.** amber **13.** boss **14.** corpulent **15.** venom **16.** node **19.** tit **20.** warren **24.** silk

WHICH BIRD AM I? (p. 23):
1. Secretarybird **2.** Flamingo **3.** Blue crane **4.** Spotted eagle owl **5.** Martial eagle **6.** Fiscal shrike or Jacky hangman **7.** Ground hornbill **8.** Fish eagle

MULTIPLE CHOICE QUIZ 5 (p. 24)
1. c: Female **2.** c: Female **3.** b: Storms River Falls **4.** b: In the Free State **5.** a: A bird **6.** c: At the end of its tail **7.** b: Oxpecker **8.** c: Insects **9.** b: A bird **10.** c: Carcasses **11.** b: White **12.** a: Male **13.** c: Furniture **14.** a: A pack **15.** a: Its appearance **16.** a: A monkey **17.** c: leaves. **18.** c: to protect its vulnerable parts from predators. **19.** b: rubber tree. **20.** c: 15 minutes

WORDSEARCH: FIND THE MAMMALS (p. 26)

B	A	T	E	R	H	B	H	Y	A	E	N	A	E	N	C	A	R	A	C	A	L	R	H	J
E	R	H	J	D	Z	J	I	U	Y	T	Q	A	E	R	H	J	Y	R	B	N	R	H	P	O
I	U	Y	T	R	P	T	Y	R	B	N	A	R	I	U	Y	T	B	U	S	H	B	A	B	Y
Y	R	I	N	Y	O	R	E	R	H	J	D	D	Y	R	B	N	U	E	R	H	J	R	B	B
R	H	M	D	D	R	B	I	U	Y	T	R	V	R	H	J	D	F	I	U	Y	T	E	J	J
E	R	P	J	B	C	B	Y	R	B	N	Y	A	I	U	Y	T	F	Y	R	B	N	B	T	T
I	U	A	T	J	U	J	R	H	J	D	D	R	Y	R	B	N	A	R	H	J	D	J	R	R
Y	R	L	N	T	P	H	W	E	M	O	N	K	E	Y	G	H	L	O	E	L	A	N	D	B
R	H	A	D	R	I	E	U	Y	R	B	N	Y	M	E	R	H	O	U	Y	T	U	Y	T	J
M	U	Y	T	B	N	D	E	R	H	G	D	D	Y	E	R	H	J	R	B	N	S
O	R	B	N	J	E	P	I	U	Y	E	R	Q	F	I	U	Y	T	R	A	T	E	R	H	Q
U	E	R	H	J	D	E	R	H	E	N	H	J	O	Y	R	B	N	E	E	R	H	J	B	U
S	H	J	B	A	B	O	O	N	I	E	Y	T	X	R	E	L	E	P	H	A	N	T	J	I
E	E	L	H	J	E	R	H	J	Y	T	B	N	E	R	H	J	D	E	Y	R	B	N	H	R
B	I	I	Y	T	E	R	H	J	R	H	J	D	R	A	B	B	I	T	R	H	J	D	Y	R
J	Y	O	B	N	B	U	S	H	P	I	G	E	U	Y	R	B	N	Y	M	E	R	H	J	E
H	R	N	J	D	V	U	Y	T	U	Y	T	D	E	R	H	J	S	E	R	V	A	L	T	L
E	E	L	I	W	N	R	B	N	R	L	E	O	P	A	R	D	R	Q	E	Y	R	B	N	B
S	P	R	I	N	G	B	O	K	Y	M	C	U	Y	T	E	R	H	C	H	E	E	T	A	H

WHAT'S THAT WORD? 3 (p. 27):
1. B **2.** A **3.** C **4.** B **5.** C **6.** C **7.** C **8.** B **9.** A **10.** A **11.** A **12.** A

MULTIPLE CHOICE QUIZ 6 (p. 28)
1. b: A monkey **2.** a: Change colour **3.** a: A fish **4.** c: Other fish **5.** b: A bird **6.** b: Whale shark **7.** a: Operculum **8.** b: To smell **9.** a: To breathe **10.** c: In their mouths **11.** c: 60 km per hour **12.** a: Talons **13.** c: 100 000 **14.** c: Lanner Falcon. **15.** b: 400 **16.** a: By constricting it **17.** b: Same mate **18.** b: 1 **19.** b: To keep cool **20.** b: 5 to 6 weeks

CROSSWORD 4 (p. 30):
ACROSS: **3.** rhinoceros **5.** dorsal **7.** ultrasound **10.** primaries **11.** gnu **14.** alien **15.** hive **16.** gorilla **19.** comb **20.** pinna **21.** wattle **22.** tern **23.** crop
DOWN: **1.** mouse **2.** parasite **4.** infrasound **6.** nucleus **8.** speculum **9.** Cainism **10.** preening **12.** harem **13.** pelagic **15.** herb **17.** raptor **18.** scat

QUIZ 4 (p. 31)

1. spring/summer **2.** the springbok **3.** cheetah **4.** the male **5.** abalone **6.** octopus/squid **7.** so that it can find its mate **8.** a crocodile **9.** yes **10.** it is extinct **11.** no **12.** African elephants **13.** botanists **14.** bull **15.** a lion **16.** a millipede **17.** at the end of its tail **18.** Porpoises have "spade shaped" teeth, while dolphins have teeth that are conical in shape / Porpoises have small, triangular dorsal fins, while dolphins' fins are taller and curve more / Porpoises lack a distinct 'beak' like those found on many species of dolphins. **19.** spit venom **20.** the giraffe

MULTIPLE CHOICE QUIZ 7 (p. 32)

1. b: A Flamingo **2.** a: 1 to 2 weeks **3.** b: 45 **4.** c: 7 **5.** c: 5 years **6.** a: A leap **7.** b: Giraffes **8.** a: A barnacle **9.** a: Dust mite **10.** a: Mammals **11.** b: The blue whale's 'song' **12.** b: sticks its tail straight up in the air like an aerial. **13.** c: Dolphin **14.** c: 98% **15.** a: A caw **16.** b: At night **17.** b: forward-looking **18.** a: A lion **19.** c: To smell **20.** b: Digging or burrowing animals

WHICH TREE AM I? (p. 34):

1. Sausage tree **2.** Wild pear tree **3.** Baobab tree **4.** Mopane tree **5.** Marula tree **6.** Keurboom **7.** Coral tree **8.** White milkwood

WORDSEARCH: FIND THE TREES AND SHRUBS (p. 35)

A	Z	B	O	T	T	L	E	B	R	U	S	H	D	R	Y	C	H	E	S	T	N	U	T	D
B	I	U	Y	T	R	Q	E	I	U	Y	L	H	T	E	U	Y	R	B	N	Y	M	E	R	D
U	E	R	C	A	M	P	H	O	R	X	K	Y	A	D	E	R	H	J	D	D	Y	I	U	M
F	R	H	J	H	U	Y	R	B	N	C	J	E	M	P	I	U	Y	T	R	Q	E	D	R	E
F	U	C	T	C	E	R	H	J	D	Y	F	Z	B	U	Y	A	S	H	H	J	D	O	H	B
A	R	O	N	L	I	B	Y	T	R	C	D	R	O	R	B	N	Z	C	A	J	A	G	A	O
L	H	R	D	U	Y	L	E	R	H	A	A	R	T	Z	D	E	R	H	J	D	D	W	H	N
O	R	K	J	S	B	U	Z	C	A	D	V	O	I	R	B	A	O	B	A	B	R	O	J	Y
T	U	W	T	T	D	E	R	H	J	D	H	J	U	Y	R	H	J	U	Y	R	U	O	T	U
H	R	O	N	E	R	B	J	H	O	N	E	Y	S	U	C	K	L	E	I	O	R	D	N	R
O	H	O	D	R	U	U	T	R	H	J	I	O	P	I	U	Y	R	B	N	Y	H	J	D	H
R	R	D	J	L	R	S	N	U	Y	T	A	L	O	E	E	R	H	J	A	C	A	C	I	A
N	U	Y	T	E	H	H	D	R	B	N	D	R	Y	U	O	D	Q	H	J	S	U	Y	T	U
Y	R	B	N	A	R	H	J	E	T	R	U	I	M	O	P	A	N	E	T	N	B	I	O	P
B	H	J	D	F	U	Y	T	L	N	U	Y	C	F	G	T	Y	O	B	N	F	E	V	E	R
J	R	H	J	H	J	A	L	D	E	R	O	O	C	C	V	O	P	R	Y	U	E	R	Y	U
H	U	Y	T	Y	T	T	R	E	R	H	J	R	O	R	H	J	A	I	O	P	C	I	O	P
Y	R	B	N	B	N	N	U	R	U	Y	T	A	R	U	Y	T	N	D	F	G	H	D	F	G
B	E	U	G	E	N	I	A	Z	R	M	I	L	K	W	O	O	D	Z	X	C	Y	Z	X	C

MULTIPLE CHOICE QUIZ 8 (p. 36)

1. c: 3 **2.** b: A rhino **3.** b: 70 years **4.** c: Remains closed **5.** a: The Cape penduline tit **6.** c: An aardwolf **7.** c: None **8.** a: 10 m **9.** b: 40 000 **10.** a: Blue **11.** c: 1,5 km **12.** a: 150 **13.** c: Approximately 24 kg **14.** b: 3000 m **15.** a: None **16.** b: 200 litres **17.** b: 5 **18.** a: 2 **19.** b: Compound **20.** a: 40 km per hour

WHAT'S THAT WORD? 4 (p. 38):

1. B **2.** A **3.** B **4.** A **5.** C **6.** A **7.** B **8.** B **9.** A **10.** B **11.** A **12.** C

LION QUIZ (p. 39)

1. A lion **2.** 1,2 m **3.** 6 **4.** 6 - 8 weeks **5.** 13 years **6.** 3 years **7.** Yes **8.** 1,5 kg **9.** 2 - 4 **10.** 7 kg

TRUE OR FALSE? 2 (p. 40)

1. F **2.** F **3.** T **4.** F **5.** F **6.** T **7.** F **8.** F **9.** T **10.** T **11.** F **12.** F **13.** T **14.** F **15.** T

ANTELOPE & WILDEBEEST QUIZ (p. 41)

1. Eland **2.** Black wildebeest **3.** 60 - 70 km per hour **4.** Hartebeest **5.** Fruit **6.** Pronking **7.** Male **8.** 2 years **9.** 1,4 m **10.** Black

TRUE OR FALSE? 3 (p. 42)
1. T **2.** F **3.** T **4.** F **5.** T **6.** F **7.** T **8.** F **9.** T **10.** F **11.** T **12.** T **13.** T **14.** F **15.** T

INSECT QUIZ (p. 43)
1. Backbone **2.** Exoskeleton **3.** The ladybird **4.** 5 **5.** Arthropods **6.** 200 times **7.** Proboscis
8. The greenbottle fly/blowfly **9.** Shimmering green **10.** Ovipositor

TRUE OR FALSE? 4 (p. 44)
1. T **2.** T **3.** F **4.** T **5.** T **6.** T **7.** F **8.** F **9.** T **10.** T **11.** F **12.** F **13.** T **14.** T **15.** F

SPIDER QUIZ (p. 45)
1. The comb **2.** Setae **3.** Spinnerets **4.** Neurotoxin **5.** Pedipalps **6.** Baboon spider **7.** 8
8. Chelicerae **9.** Black widow **10.** Abdomen

TRUE OR FALSE? 5 (p. 46)
1. F **2.** T **3.** F **4.** T **5.** T **6.** F **7.** T **8.** F **9.** T **10.** T **11.** T **12.** T **13.** T **14.** T **15.** F

ELEPHANT QUIZ (p. 47)
1. About 3,4 m **2.** 2,5 – 3,2 tons **3.** 102,3 kg and 107,3 kg **4.** By multiplying the length of the hind footprint by 5,8 m **5.** 120 kg **6.** 3 – 8 years **7.** 60 years **8.** Shooting/poaching **9.** 120 litres **10.** 12 litres

QUIZ 5 (p. 48)
1. A hive **2.** A tsetse fly **3.** the Cape Sugarbird **4.** 3 5) Crustaceans **6.** A vulture **7.** Spots **8.** 2
9. A bullfrog **10.** Termites **11.** Penguin, Ostrich **12.** A bird **13.** 8 **14.** Its tentacles **15.** A fish
16. Native to or confined to a certain region **17.** At night **18.** The coelacanth **19.** Tusks **20.** Mane

WHAT'S THAT WORD? 5 (p. 49):
1. B **2.** B **3.** A **4.** B **5.** B **6.** C **7.** A **8.** A **9.** A **10.** C **11.** B **12.** C

FIND THE FISH (p. 50)

S	P	R	I	N	G	E	R	B	N	B	B	R	E	A	M	B	N	B	N	D	B	G	B	S
U	Y	R	B	N	Y	T	Z	J	D	J	T	E	R	H	T	J	D	J	D	O	J	U	J	T
G	R	U	N	T	E	R	Z	T	R	T	X	S	N	A	P	P	E	R	X	G	T	R	T	I
I	U	Y	T	R	E	R	B	A	S	S	U	Y	R	B	N	Y	T	U	Y	F	R	N	R	N
Y	T	E	R	H	L	U	B	N	B	E	E	R	H	S	H	A	R	K	R	I	B	A	B	G
T	R	Q	E	I	T	R	J	D	J	A	I	U	Y	T	R	Q	R	I	U	S	B	R	B	R
A	N	C	H	O	V	Y	T	R	T	H	Y	T	E	R	H	J	U	Y	T	H	J	D	J	A
Y	T	Y	V	E	U	Y	R	B	E	O	U	Y	R	B	N	Y	T	U	Y	S	T	R	T	Y
E	R	E	R	D	E	R	H	J	D	R	E	R	H	J	D	D	R	E	R	P	R	H	R	U
Y	S	N	O	E	K	E	U	Y	R	S	E	U	Y	R	B	C	A	T	F	I	S	H	Y	T
H	Y	T	C	O	P	D	E	R	H	E	D	E	R	H	J	T	E	R	H	T	E	R	H	T
E	E	R	K	F	G	E	U	Y	R	T	E	R	H	T	S	A	N	D	S	H	A	R	K	H
R	R	B	C	A	S	T	E	E	N	B	R	A	S	D	S	F	B	N	E	A	S	D	F	G
R	Y	T	O	E	U	Y	R	B	E	U	Y	R	B	E	R	O	M	A	N	N	B	C	O	D
I	E	R	D	D	E	R	H	J	D	E	R	H	J	D	E	G	T	R	E	R	B	N	Y	T
N	R	H	J	R	H	A	M	M	E	R	H	E	A	D	T	U	R	H	N	H	J	D	D	R
G	U	Y	T	U	R	H	J	R	H	J	E	V	R	H	J	R	P	I	L	C	H	A	R	D
T	T	E	R	T	U	Y	T	U	Y	T	R	C	U	Y	T	N	B	N	Y	E	R	H	J	G
S	E	V	E	N	T	Y	F	O	U	R	R	K	T	E	R	S	T	U	M	P	N	O	S	E

WHICH REPTILE AM I? (p. 51):
1. A crocodile **2.** A chameleon **3.** Brown house snake **4.** A leopard tortoise **5.** A gecko
6. Black mamba **7.** Boomslang **8.** African rock python